Mystery

SHIVERS

Mystery

by Terry Deary

WATTS BOOKS
London · New York · Sydney

This edition 1997

Watts Books

96 Leonard Street

London EC2A 4RH

Franklin Watts

14 Mars Road

Lane Cove

NSW

UK ISBN: 0 7496 2182 6

Dewey Decimal Classification 001.9

Editor: Rosemary McCormick

Designer: Mike Davis, Ian Probert

Author: Terry Deary

Cover Artist: Mark Taylor

Line Illustrator: Rob Mooney

Contents

The following titles are also available:

Terror
Spooks
Disaster

Introduction

When night falls you can look up to the stars and contemplate the vastness of the universe. In the face of such enormity you can believe that almost anything is possible. You can feel forces that feeble humans do not comprehend. Forces that could make things happen that we just don't understand.

Mysteries. Could these forces make the living disappear off the face of the earth? Can they make the dead come back to life? Are they to blame for reports of strange lights in the sky and monstrous creatures in the oceans?

Or are there simple, boring explanations for all these strange happenings? For in this world of mystery there are frauds and fools.

The frauds tell the lies . . . the fools believe them.

All you can do is look at the facts . . . then make up your own mind.

The stories in this book are all based on reports that someone, somewhere, has sworn are true. Their fact files may spill some light into the shadows that hide the truth. Or they may hide that truth darker and deeper than ever.

So, open up the book . . . and let in a little darkness.

1. Mystery of the Waxworks

Some places are built to scare people. Waxwork museums can be frightening places. There are many mysterious tales told about wax figures. They are just silly stories. A lifeless, wax dummy can't harm you . . . can it?

Sacramento – 1857*

Ten cents to see the waxworks, ma'am. Ten cents for you, five for the boy. That's right. Through that door, and turn right.

What? Guided tours? No, I don't give guided tours. You see I have to stay here at the door and collect the money, don't I?

Pay me! You'll pay me to give you a tour? Hah! Heck, no, ma'am. No, no, no. Not for a dollar. Why, to tell the truth . . . to tell the honest truth . . . you wouldn't get me through that door for a hundred dollars. No, nor a million dollars come to that. Wild

9

horses wouldn't drag me into Mr Turner's Waxwork Theatre, ma'am.

Why not? Well . . . heck, ma'am, I wouldn't want to scare you and the little boy. Let's just say I used to go in there when Mr Turner first opened the place. I was caretaker in those days. I used to go in every night after we closed. Clean up after the people. Sweep out, polish the glass cases. You wouldn't believe the sticky finger marks they left on the glass. Why, I even used to give the old waxwork figures a dust.

Never again! No, you just go on in there with the boy and enjoy yourselves.

You want what? You want me to tell you what I'm scared of? Mr Turner wouldn't like that, ma'am. He doesn't want me scaring the public away. It's more than my job's worth!

You'll *pay* me? Just to tell you my story! Heck, ma'am, I couldn't take your money. A dollar? No, no, no! You what? You did say five dollars? Now that's mighty tempting, ma'am.

Look, it's quiet. Nearly closing time. If you and the boy promise . . . cross your hearts and hope to die . . . then I might just tell you the story. Pull up that chair. That's right, you'll be better sitting down in case you faint with the terror. And that would never do, would it? Eh?

That's right . . . are you comfortable? Good. Now where was I? Oh, yeah . . . er, that five dollars. Thanks! It's the best five dollars you'll ever spend. Think of the evenings you'll have, entertaining your friends with a truly mysterious story.

It all started soon after we opened this place back

in 1857. Mr Turner had seen the Madame Tussaud's waxworks exhibition over in London. He came back to Sacramento just about the time of the gold rush. There were hundreds of miners with thousands of dollars to spend. Mr Turner had the waxwork figures made and opened up this here museum.

I was his first caretaker. I used to enjoy the job at first. So many models of famous people. The presidents of the United States. The Pilgrim Fathers and what have you.

But the miners were a rough lot. They wanted something more exciting. More thrilling. More *chilling.*

So Mr Turner had the guillotine scene built. You ever heard of the French Revolution? 'Course you have, ma'am, an educated lady like you. Hundreds of people losing their heads because the government didn't like them. We had a guillotine built – it didn't really work, of course! But we put some shiny red paint on the blade to make it look good and bloody.

Sorry, you're not feeling faint, are you, ma'am? The little boy's turned a bit green at the gills too. You want me to go on to the really scary bit? OK.

Mr Turner had models made of the poor people just about to be executed by the guillotine. He arranged them in a group. There was the executioner, of course, and there was some woman who'd just come to watch the killings. She was sitting there knitting and enjoying it all. And of course there was a victim with his neck on the block and his head over the basket.

We had the lights way down low and it was spooky, I can tell you. Spooky. Why, I knew they were just waxworks, I'd helped set them up myself! But, boy, they still gave me the creeps!

There was one figure in particular. A guy in a black suit with a cruel face. The label said he was called Nicodème Leopold-Lepide. It seemed like those old glass eyes of his stared right through you. No matter where you went in the room those eyes followed you and sent shivers up your spine, tickled the hairs on the back of your neck and sent those shivers right back down again.

Still it was my job. Old Leopold-Lepide was popular enough with the visitors. I tried to ignore him. But one morning I went in and couldn't ignore him any longer.

It was dark, of course . . . no windows in the museum. I just took an oil lamp in the room with me to start cleaning. Put the lamp down on a table and started sweeping. Then I saw something on the floor glinting in the light. Two eyes staring at me. Leopold-Lepide's eyes looking up at me from the floor. His head was just lying there in the dust.

Did I what? Pick it up? No, ma'am, I didn't! Nothing in Heaven or Hell would get me to touch that head. What did I do? I went straight to Mr Turner.

"Somebody must have got in during the night, Ezra," he said.

"No, sir. I locked it last night. Nobody but you and me have keys."

"Must be a weakness in the model," he said. "I'll have it fixed."

And he did. But it did no good. Every morning after that I went in only to find that the figure had moved. After two weeks Mr Turner said, "Look, Ezra, we got to stay inside tonight. See what happens!"

Like a fool I agreed! I thought if Mr Turner was game enough to stay in there then I wasn't going to look a coward. So we got ourselves a couple of chairs. Comfortable chairs. Too comfortable! We fell asleep.

The cold woke me up. The lamp was burning low. I turned up the wick . . . and saw those eyes staring up at me . . . from the floor.

So next night we filled ourselves up with coffee to stay awake. That's when Mr Turner told me about that Leopold-Lepide character. It seems old Leo was a tax collector. Squeezed the poor French peasants out of their last sou. They were glad to see him executed.

When he'd finished the story Mr Turner asked, "What time is it, Ezra?" I looked at my pocket watch. "Nearly two-thirty," I said.

He rubbed his eyes and stared at the guillotine scene. His voice dropped to a whisper. "Ezra!" he croaked. "Look!"

I turned the lamp up. Those eyes were staring at me. I mean straight at me! And that wasn't a wax skin. It was too . . . too real! The arm moved first. Slowly, but it was moving. Then the legs. It turned to face us. Then the face moved . . . that was the worst of all. It was frowning!

Last of all the lips moved. And it spoke. True as I'm sitting here, that waxwork spoke to Mr Turner and me. What did it say? Heck, ma'am, I don't rightly know. See, it spoke in French! But Mr Turner spoke a bit of French. He told me later.

Seems Leopold-Lepide said, "Can I not get any

13

peace? Not even at night? The French people came in their hundreds to see us executed. Now they come to see our spirits trapped in wax. Stay away . . . or you'll be sorry!"

What did we do? We got the heck out of it, ma'am! And, like I say, the hounds of Hell wouldn't get me back in there at night.

Witnesses? Now it's strange you should say that. Mr Turner and me took some strong liquor to calm our nerves. And the drink loosened our tongues. We told our story over in the Last Chance Saloon. A young newspaper feller heard of it. Said he wouldn't believe it unless he saw it for himself.

What did Mr Turner do? What could he do? He let the feller spend the night in there. Of course that reporter had to go in *alone*!

We closed the museum for the night. Gave him a lantern and a chair . . . and locked him in. Oh, yes, we locked him in . . . we had to make sure there were no tricks.

I guess I must have nodded off. The first thing I remember was hearing his screams. He was hammering at the door, trying to get out. By the time I got it open he almost fell into my arms. Dead? No, not dead . . . but if I hadn't got that door open I guess he would have been. But at least we knew it wasn't just Mr Turner and me making it up.

I still got the young man's story on me here somewhere. Here, in this pocket. Of course it's a bit creased now. This all happened twenty years ago. But I can tell you what it says . . . heck, I know it off by heart. This is what he says . . .

As I sat in the gloom of the lantern, the dim flickering light fell on the rows which were so strangely like human beings. Their stillness made them seem even more strange and ghastly. I listened for the sound of their breathing and the rustle of their clothes.

For an hour or two I sat facing these figures and felt brave enough. I mean, they were only waxworks . . . And waxworks don't move. But every time I looked away from the tax collector then looked back he seemed to be in a slightly different pose.

I kept looking until I saw something. The waxwork's arm did move. Slowly at first, then faster it raised its two hands. Suddenly it snapped off its head! I stared, terrified, gripping the chair. Then, to make it worse, the wax head was replaced by a ghostly face. And that face had the cruellest, most evil sneer you ever saw.

It moved down from its stand. I jumped to my feet and stood to face it. The most frightening thing was that I could see clean through its head!

I backed into the door. I tapped on it. I wanted Ezra Potter to see this for himself. But there was no answer! He was asleep! I banged harder while the *ghost came closer. I turned my back on it and hammered on the door. I screamed when I felt those greasy wax hands on my neck. I screamed again . . . then I think I fainted. The next I knew I woke up in Ezra Potter's arms.*

I swear by all that's holy that this story is true.

There it is in black and white, sure as you're sitting there. Mr Turner and me we found the head lying on the floor beside the guillotine. But the body was beside the door. And the wax fingers were flat on the ends . . . as if they'd squeezed something hard.

You look a bit pale, ma'am. You sure you want to go in and see the waxworks?

No? But you've paid your ten cents and five for the boy!

Oh, don't worry . . . old Leopold-Lepide's waxwork was melted down. We haven't had a scrap of trouble since then.

You sure? And I can keep the money? That's mighty generous of you, ma'am.

Call again, any time . . . and don't forget to tell your friends.

I guess it's time to lock up anyway.

Goodnight, ma'am . . . and, oh, ma'am . . .

Sweet dreams!

Mystery of the waxworks — VERDICT

The waxwork story caused a sensation in all the American newspapers of the day. The most amazing was, of course, the article written by a man who had seen the waxwork moving for himself. There are many explanations for this strange story. Here are just five. Which one do you prefer . . . or can you think of a better one?

1. The nightmare
The owner, the caretaker and the reporter were frightened men. They believed that the waxwork was possessed by an evil spirit. They didn't really see it move, but they were so terrified they imagined that it moved. They suffered from hallucinations – a sort of waking nightmare. The waxwork was really harmless, but a weak joint kept making the head drop off.

2. The liars
Richard Turner wanted to make money. Lots of money. His waxwork show was rather dull and boring. So he made up a story about a living, moving waxwork to bring in curious customers. The caretaker, Ezra Potter, swore the story was true because he was well paid by Richard Turner to tell that story. The newspaper reporter went along with the lies; it made a good story and he'd sell more papers.

3. The fraud

Richard Turner and Ezra Potter made up the story to attract customers. They hired an actor to dress up as the waxwork and the actor took his place just before the reporter was locked in the room. He 'came to life' after a couple of hours and scared the reporter half to death.

4. The joker

Someone was playing a practical joke on Turner, Potter and the reporter. They knew of a secret entrance to the museum and were able to sneak in each night and knock the head off the tax collector model. When Turner and Potter spent the night in the museum they saw the joker moving around. They were so terrified they didn't wait to see exactly what (or who) was moving about in the shadows. They panicked and ran. The newspaper reporter made the same mistake.

5. The ghost

The ghost of Leopold-Lepide returned to haunt the waxworks. It possessed the waxwork figure and acted out losing its head every night. It was furious that people still came to stare at it. The ghost had the power to make the waxwork move and speak. It warned the owner and the caretaker not to bother it at night. When the reporter appeared it finally lost its temper and attacked him.

What do you think?

An equally gruesome 'mummy' story concerns an exhibit at a Californian amusement park. For fifty years the Horror House showed a mysterious figure and claimed it was a mummified body. It chilled people and they happily paid to see it . . . but in their hearts they didn't really believe it was a corpse underneath the bandages. They knew it was a dummy, not a mummy.

In December 1976 a television company decided to film in the Horror House – they were making an episode of a popular serial called The Six Million Dollar Man. *In the crowded little room a cameraman bumped into the mummy and its arm fell off . . . to reveal human bones and dried flesh underneath!*

The corpse was rushed to a doctor. Police suspected it was a murder victim who'd been cunningly hidden in the Horror House! The doctor confirmed that the man had died of a bullet wound . . . but he'd been dead for eighty years or so.

Still, there is a mystery as to who this man was. One theory is that he was a famous Oklahoma outlaw called Elmer McCurdy. McCurdy robbed trains and banks in the 1900s. When he was killed in a shoot-out with lawmen there was no one to pay for his funeral. The undertaker decided to make some money by mummifying Elmer and charging people to see him. He later sold the mummy to a carnival and so it arrived at the amusement park.

In 1977 the mummy was taken and given a proper

burial at the famous outlaw cemetery of Boot Hill.
Let's hope it really was Elmer McCurdy . . . or there
could be a very confused corpse wondering how it
ended up in Boot Hill!

2. Mystery of the Alien Strangers

Is there anyone out there? Beyond this planet that we know, are there other worlds, other life forms? What are they like and what do they want? And, if there are such alien beings, have they found us before we can find them?

Dartmoor, England – 1987

We should be dead. We should have died of cold that winter night.

Dartmoor on a December night is no place for two humans to walk. But we were desperate. The wind swept in over the freezing Atlantic Ocean and carried flecks of stinging snow. They melted on our thin anoraks, soaked through, and the wind turned that damp to ice against our skins.

Death by exposure is a strange thing. After the first shock of the chill you don't notice the cold so much. You become sleepy and stop caring about anything.

You give up trying. That's when you sink to certain death.

We huddled together but not for warmth. Simply for the comfort of being together. My wife, Meg, clutched at my arm. I was already feeling drowsy and slipping away. She was stronger and kept me awake by talking. "Don't go to sleep, Dave," she urged. "It'll soon be light. Help can't be far away."

She was lying, of course. It was just after midnight. Help and daylight were still eight hours away. We'd be dead by then.

"Go on," I mumbled, knowing my numb lips were slurring the words. "Get back to the car. You should be safe in there."

"I'm not going anywhere without you," she said. Stubborn. Meg's always been stubborn.

"And I'm not going anywhere with this twisted ankle," I groaned. My body was numb with the cold. The only part that wasn't numb was the twisted ankle. It was burning with a pain that ran up my leg. It was keeping me awake when all I wanted to do was fall asleep. I no longer cared if I didn't wake up.

"Why don't you keep going towards that light we saw?" I mumbled. "We must have been nearly there before I fell. Maybe there's a house . . . and help."

"I wouldn't get twenty steps down this path, Dave," she sighed. "It's a swamp. If we're going to die we might as well die together."

And that was that. We'd both decided we were going to die. There was nothing to do but wait.

How do people get themselves into this sort of mess? Easily. When we left home that morning it was a bright, sunny Christmas Eve. Meg and I were going to stay with friends in Cornwall. We packed a few clothes in a suitcase and dropped them in the car. We didn't pack thick winter clothes because we didn't expect to spend much time outside in the cold. After all, we were going to a warm, comfortable cottage, weren't we?

It seemed as if everybody else had the same idea: travel south for Christmas. The traffic grew worse and it was getting later and later. That's why we decided to take a shortcut straight across the moor. The lonely, grim, deserted moor on a winter's night. It was a bad decision.

The car was old and as it began to freeze outside, it became almost as chilly inside. My hands became stiff with the cold and our breath began to freeze on the windscreen. There was no way I could drive another twenty miles like that. "I think we should turn round," Meg said.

"I'm not even sure if we should try to make it back to the last town," I said through my chattering teeth. "Let's just look for the nearest house and stop to ask for help. Even a cup of hot coffee."

I turned the car on the slippery road and began to head back the way we'd come. The moor was bleak and black on either side of the snow-dusted road. Suddenly Meg called out, "A light! On the right. Take the next turn on the right!"

I stepped hard on the brake and swung the car to the right. It was the wrong thing to do, of course. The car slid sideways and missed the turning. It ended with the back wheels in a ditch. I crashed it into low gear and tried to drive out again. We didn't move. I opened the door and let a blast of freezing air into the car. The door was open long enough for me to see the wheels were half buried in mud. There was no way the car could move without being towed.

"Sorry," I said.

Meg shook her head. "No. It was my fault. I was sure I saw a light." We peered through a hole scraped in the ice on the screen. There was nothing.

"Maybe they've switched it off," I said. "If there's a track then there must be something up there."

"Want to try?" Meg asked.

"We can't stay here," I said. "We'd be better off walking. It'll warm us up."

That was the second stupid decision we made that night. The track was an unmade road, deep ruts made us stumble and icy mud made us slip. Our town shoes, of course, were useless and soaked through within ten steps.

Then my foot slithered off a rut and came to a sudden stop when it hit a rock. I think Meg heard the crack as the ligament snapped from the bone. I gave a sharp cry and slid to the ground. I didn't mind the muddy water seeping through my best trousers. Nothing at all mattered except the pain.

Of course, Meg refused to leave me. I couldn't go on towards the light. I couldn't even get back to the shelter of the car. As the wind off the moor wrapped us in its blanket of cold I just knew we were going to die.

Then they came.

I can't explain what happened next – I can still

scarcely believe it. But Meg was with me. She saw the same as I did, so I didn't just dream it.

They came. First the light. A searchlight beam shone down on us. Then the sound. A trembling in the air like a never-ending roll of distant thunder.

Then the light snapped off and, without its dazzling glare, we could see where it had come from.

It looked like a building. A huge dome taller than two houses. It had its own glowing green light inside. I wondered how a building that size could suddenly have appeared. Had we been so close to safety but not seen it through the blizzard?

Before I had time for further thought a door opened and three figures stepped out. Almost human in shape, but thin. Much too thin. We couldn't see their faces because they were hidden behind what looked like breathing masks. The strangers obviously didn't feel the cold. They wore only thin black suits.

They stopped. One of them handed me a small bowl. Its voice sounded in my head rather than in my ears. "Drink," it said. "It will do you good."

I did as instructed. The liquid had no flavour but it warmed me like a glass of hot whisky. All at once the throbbing pain in my leg was eased and I felt strong enough to stand. However, as I put my weight on the damaged ankle it gave way and I stumbled forward.

One of the strangers ran a hand over the leg. "Damaged ligament. No broken bone. It will heal," he announced. Then he picked me up. He may have been thin but his arms were as strong as a fork-lift truck. He carried me back towards the car and all the time his voice was running through my head. "The woman will drive. I will place you in the passenger seat. We will then move you to a place where you will be safe. Trust us. Whatever you do, you must not move."

We reached the car in a minute and he placed me carefully through the passenger door and closed it behind me. Even though he was outside in the howling wind his voice came to me as clear as ever. "Remember. Do not try to move."

Meg climbed into the driver's seat and sat silent. We didn't dare speak. There was nothing to say that would have made any sense.

The snow had eased slightly now. Through the graceful stream of white flakes we could see the three black figures as they walked back to the green, glowing building. They stepped through the doorway and it closed behind them.

A few moments later my stomach lurched. I thought we were sinking into the ground. In fact it was because my brain couldn't make sense of what it was seeing. The car wasn't sinking. That huge building was rising. Rising smoothly into the air as smoothly as a child's balloon.

Then it drifted towards us and hovered over us. I wanted to jump out of the car and run. "Don't try to move," Meg said. That was what the stranger had told us.

It's easier said than done when an invisible force begins to lift your car into the air and carry you over an empty moor. If it dropped us now we would be lost for ever, I thought as I looked down on the rough rocky landscape dotted with glistening mud swamps.

Its speed was incredible. It seemed less than a

minute before we were hovering over the orange ribbons of light that showed a road leading into a town. We began to drop and I had the sickening feeling that you get in a speeding lift. Yet the car was placed on the road as gently as the fat snowflakes that were landing on the windscreen.

We were alone on the road. Nothing in the sky but heavy clouds. Snow fell quietly, stained orange by the street lamps. There was no green glow. Whatever that dome had been it had dropped us and moved off quickly before anyone else had seen it.

We drove into the town, found a hotel and warmed ourselves. Meg and I were young and it did not take us long to recover from our harrowing experience. But one thing we won't get over so quickly is the meeting with those rescuers.

We've talked about it many times. We are both quite sure that whatever we met on the moor that night wasn't human.

Those creatures in black had to be aliens. They have found our planet and they have begun to explore it. They are keeping their presence secret but will reveal themselves if they see humans in danger as Meg and I were.

The good news is that they are friendly and caring.

One day everyone will meet these aliens and they will know that we didn't imagine it . . . or invent the story.

UFOs — Make up your mind

Meg and David told no one of their experience for two years – they were afraid they would be laughed at. Finally they confided in friends who suggested they repeat their story to a group of people who collected UFO reports.

Many people believe there is no mystery as far as Unidentified Flying Objects are concerned. As David says, they are alien creatures from some other planets.

People have used this idea to explain not only UFOs but great earthly wonders, from the building of the Egyptian pyramids to the appearances of the Loch Ness Monster.

On 24 June 1947 pilot Kenneth Arnold took off from an airport in Washington State, USA, to search for a missing plane. As he was circling he saw a flash of light in the sky and reported, "I saw, far to my left and to the north, a formation of nine very bright objects coming from the area of Mount Baker. They were flying very close to the mountain tops and travelling with tremendous speed. I could see no tails on them and they flew like no aircraft I had ever seen before. They were like saucers skipping across water."

The next day the newspapers came up with a new phrase that people have used ever since . . . Flying Saucers.

Within six months there were many sightings and US Airforce pilots had orders to shoot down any of these saucers. The US government believed they could be a *new Russian secret weapon! A government agency called Project Bluebook was set up to investigate these sightings and at one point was receiving 30 sightings every day. After twenty years (and $500,000 spent) Project Bluebook was closed down. It reported that there were no secret Russian weapons . . . and no flying saucers either.*

There are arguments for and against the idea of alien visitors and their UFOs . . .

The case for alien visitors

There have been reports of flying saucers for many centuries – 300 reports had been collected prior to the year 1900. One of the earliest was a report of glowing discs in the skies of Switzerland in 1566.

Witnesses who have met aliens have sometimes taken lie-detector tests. These often prove that they are telling the truth.

Some sightings have been backed up with recordings of radar pictures showing unexplained "blips" on the screen.

There have been many photographs of flying saucers. The first was taken in 1883 and the Victorians' interest in alien invaders grew from that. By 1893 the author H. G. Wells had written a popular book about an alien invasion called War of the Worlds. *Many photographs have appeared since then. Some are obviously faked – others have been examined in minute detail and experts have confirmed they are not trick photographs.*

Reports have come from highly respected people, including former United States President Jimmy Carter who, in 1973, saw "a UFO that looked as big as the moon and changed colour several times from red to green". When he became president he ordered a $20 million investigation into UFOs.

The case against alien visitors

Many, if not most, cases of UFO sightings turn out to be false. So called photographs of alien spacecraft have been scientifically proven to be such things as saucepan lids photographed as they were thrown into the air. Many kinds of trick photography have been used as well. There have also been numerous reports of aliens "kidnapping" humans on quiet country roads, but there is no real evidence to support these claims.

In the 1950s a man claimed to have been lifted into an alien spacecraft, and examined before being released. He became famous and made a lot of money from re-telling the story. Thirty years later he admitted he had made the whole story up.

If there are aliens out there then there must be dozens of alien races from dozens of distant planets who are exploring our world. For every report of meetings with aliens seems to describe a different creature. Many of them look vaguely human but reports have described:

Appearance

- *5 metre figure with blood-red face and glowing green eyes*
- *1 metre figure with huge eyes, no eyelids, no nose, a slit for a mouth and pointed ears – his feet were webbed and his skin silver*
- *bush with a large golden eye on top and smaller eyes on its lower branches*
- *little white creatures like dolls*

Movement

- *walking like a human*
- *floating*
- *riding along a beam of light*
- *disappearing and appearing somewhere else*

Space ships

- *30 metre high vessel, glowing purple, the shape of an electric light bulb*
- *2 metre high dome standing on legs*
- *globe as big as a house*
- *silvery disc like the underside of a dinner plate*
- *orange clouds*

Scientists generally do not believe in alien visitors. Most sightings can be explained away as weather balloons, shooting stars, cloud formations, aeroplane navigation lights, planets or stars.

Modern technology – cameras, video and radar have all been used by UFO spotters. While they have come up with a lot of unexplained sightings, they haven't yet come up with anything which conclusively proves that aliens have landed on our planet.

3. Mystery of the Invisible Thief

Every minute, everywhere in the world, there are crimes being committed. Millions of them. Yet some are remembered and talked about forever. They are the mysteries that have no explanation ... or the ones that have several explanations ...

Portland, Oregon, USA – 24 November 1971
Tina Mucklow was happy. She stood at the top of the stairway and welcomed the passengers on board the Boeing 727. Tonight everyone was happy.

As a stewardess she had her fair share of grumpy passengers. The tired, the nervous, the impatient and the moody. But today was different. Today was Thanksgiving Day.

"Good evening, sir!" she smiled, and a warm smile was returned. "Seat D 32, sir, that's a window seat just forward of the wing."

"Thank you, miss," the man said.

"No, thank *you*, sir. Thank you for flying with Northwest Airlines. Have a good journey."

"Oh, I will. I'm off home for Thanksgiving," the man replied happily. "I'll see the kids for the first time in weeks."

"That's nice. I'll tell Captain Scott to fly just a bit faster, shall I?" Tina joked.

The man grinned wider and stepped into the aircraft.

The hostess looked at her watch. Four minutes to take-off and all the passengers on her list were on board. She began to signal for the stairs to be removed but waited when she spied a figure hurrying across the tarmac towards her. She blew on her hands as the icy wind whipped around the side of the fuselage and chilled her.

The man was nothing special. Average height and build. Just a canvas bag clutched to his chest. His head was bent into the wind.

He hurried up the stairs and she wondered why he was wearing tinted glasses on a winter's evening. Tina's smile was wasted on him. He didn't look up as she greeted him. "Good evening, sir, you don't have a reservation?"

"Just bought the ticket," he mumbled and thrust it towards her. She checked it. It was fine. Evening flight to Seattle, Washington. Name of D. B. Cooper. An ordinary name. But it was a name that Tina was never going to forget if she lived to be a hundred.

"No window seats left, Mr Cooper . . ." she began.

"Don't want one. Aisle seat," he said gruffly and kept his chin tucked into his chest. "Thank you," he added as an afterthought.

"No problem, sir," she said and checked her passenger list. "Can I put your bag in the luggage locker?"

"No . . . I'll need it on the flight."

"Some of you gentlemen never stop working," she smiled. "Take C13 on your left."

"Right," he said and stepped into the plane, still clutching that canvas bag.

At last she felt they were ready to leave. The steps rolled away and she swung the door shut. She expected the next half-hour to be her busiest time. Everyone would want serving meals and drinks at once. After they'd all been served it would ease off. Then she'd be able to put her feet up in the crew room and have a coffee herself.

Tina had about six orders in her head when she approached C13. Mr Cooper seemed to have written his order down. That would help, she thought as she took the note and read it.

At first she thought it was a mistake. This wasn't an order for food. She read again. She read it slowly, taking in every word. The note said:

I have a bomb with me. If I don't get $200,000 I will blow us all to bits.

He pointed to the canvas bag on his knee. He opened it slightly and let her see the sticks of dynamite inside. Tina looked around at the passengers, eating, chatting, laughing. "Excuse me, sir," she said as calmly as she could manage. "I'll just take your . . . er, *request* . . . to Captain Scott."

Trying not to wobble on her heels, she walked

down the aisle. The frightened stewardess stumbled through the door into the flight deck and silently pushed the note into the pilot's hand. He looked up at her.

"Passenger in C13. Cooper. D. B. Cooper," she said. "I've seen the . . . thing in his bag. I don't think he's bluffing."

Captain Scott nodded before pressing a switch on his control panel and speaking into a microphone. "Hijack – hijack – hijack!" he repeated calmly.

The response from control was almost instant. By the time the Boeing had landed in Seattle the FBI hijack team was in place.

Marksmen with high-power rifles trained their sights on the plane as it taxied to a halt. Tina walked down the aisle and tried to smile. "Sorry, ladies and gentlemen, but there will be a short delay in disembarking. Please remain in your seats."

The passengers groaned and some of their good humour began to disappear.

Only one man ignored her. The man in C13. He unfastened his seat belt and walked quickly to the cabin. "Don't look around. Just do as you are told," he said to Captain Scott. "Tell the FBI to get that money onto the plane."

"They won't have it yet . . ." Captain Scott began.

"Don't try to stall for time, Captain," Cooper said quietly. "I am quite sure that the money will be there. It always is. Now, as soon as I have seen it I will allow the passengers to leave the plane."

Scott shrugged and passed the message to ground control.

"And don't forget . . . I want two backpack parachutes and two chestpack parachutes."

Five minutes later, Tina Mucklow brought the white sack of money to the cabin. Cooper sat in the corner of the cabin and continued to give his orders. "Now we can let the passengers off this plane . . . we'll refuel and get moving again, shall we?"

"Where to?" the captain asked.

Cooper shook his head. "You take off, Captain. *Then* I'll tell you where we're going."

Half an hour later the Boeing was airborne again and Cooper was giving new orders. "Mexico, Captain . . . but I want you to fly slowly with the wheels down and the flaps down."

"Sorry, Mr Cooper, we'll use too much fuel that way. We'd never reach Mexico," he said.

"Then stop for fuel," Cooper ordered.

"That will have to be Reno," Captain Scott said.

"Fine," the hijacker said with a brisk nod. "Now, give me back my note, miss."

"Your note?" Tina asked.

"I am not stupid enough to leave a clue like that for the FBI to work on. The note, please, miss," he repeated.

The stewardess pulled it from her jacket pocket and handed it over. He glanced at it then put it carefully inside his own jacket. For the first time his eyes met hers. She could see the strain behind the tinted glasses though his voice stayed calm. "Now, Captain, lower the rear loading ramp."

Tina glanced through the cabin windows. Seattle airport was just ribbons of light below them. The lights were falling away. But two sets of lights were steadier. They were moving alongside the Boeing about a mile away. She knew they'd be the Air Force jets tracking them. If Cooper saw them he didn't show it. Perhaps, she thought, he didn't care.

The pilot flicked a switch and a red warning light came on. Cooper backed towards the cabin door. "I'll be in my seat. Lock this door behind me and don't open it . . . or else."

The noise in the cabin was deafening as the engines strained to hold the slow speed. The crew in the cabin spoke only when necessary. Captain Scott talked calmly to the government agents on the ground. Tina sat on the floor. Her legs seemed weak. Just half an hour later Captain Scott made a slight snatching movement at the controls. "He's gone," he said.

"Who? Cooper?" Tina asked.

"Yes. Something made the tail section buck just a little. He's jumped."

"Where are we?" she asked.

The navigator checked his chart. "Just over the border with Oregon," he said.

"What's there?" Tina wondered aloud.

"Nothing," the navigator replied. "Nothing except mountains and forests."

"So, he got away with it," Tina exclaimed.

"No. He's a dead man," Captain Scott said calmly before speaking into the microphone. "Hijacker has bailed out."

"The fighter planes saw nothing," came the response.

"Never mind. Wait till daylight. You can pick up

38

the money then – along with the pieces of Mr D. B. Cooper. Staying on course for Reno. Roger and out."

Tina reached for the door. "No!" Captain Scott said. "I could be wrong. He could still be out there. Let's just check first, shall we?" He switched on the speaker into the passenger compartment. "Mr Cooper. I am now going to raise the rear ramp in order to land. Can you come forward to the cabin, let me know if that's OK?"

There was no reply. "Shall I look?" Tina offered.

"Go ahead."

The stewardess opened the door a little and peered through. Seat C13 was empty. She opened it wider. She was more nervous now than when Cooper had handed her the note. "Mr Cooper?" she called above the roar of the engines. "He's gone, Captain Scott," she announced.

The pilot's shoulders relaxed. "A madman," he said. "What a way to die."

"He had a parachute," Tina said.

"I was in the Air Force, Miss Mucklow. The air above the mountains is very thin – it will hardly slow him. I reckon he'll be doing forty miles an hour when he hits the ground – ground which he won't even see in this light. Of course he'll hardly feel it . . . with that thin coat and trousers he'll probably be a block of ice when he hits the ground! Mark my words, they'll find a parachute, a body and a bag of dollars. And even if he survives the jump he'll have to be some kind of expert woodsman to find his way back to civilisation."

"But if he *does* . . .?" Tina persisted.

"Then good luck to him. If he survives the drop

he's earned every cent. But take my word for it, he won't survive. Mr D. B. Cooper will be spending that money in Heaven . . . or Hell."

"They'll never find him," Tina stubbornly announced.

"Sooner or later something will turn up," he insisted. "A parachute, a body, or a dollar."

She always enjoyed her arguments with Captain Bill Scott.

After the crime, the police and army searched the Oregon mountains and found nothing. Not a parachute, not a body, not a dollar. Then, three weeks later, a typewritten letter arrived at a newspaper office that bore the signature of D. B. Cooper. She could still remember it and still felt guilty. Guilty because she was secretly glad that the little man had survived. He was a thief; he'd threatened to kill 150 people; but she couldn't help wishing him well. That letter sounded like him. It said . . .

I am not a modern-day Robin Hood. Unfortunately I have just 14 months to live. The hijack was the safest way I could find to buy myself happiness and freedom for those few brief months. I didn't rob Northwest Airlines because I thought it would be exciting or heroic. I don't blame people for hating me. Nor do I blame anybody for wanting me caught or punished – though this can never happen. I knew from the start I would never be caught. I've come and gone on several airline flights since the hijack and I am not hiding away in some small town. Nor am I a criminal lunatic – I have never even received a speeding ticket.

That made Tina smile at the time.

"It's a fake," Captain Scott had said. "He took that hijack note from you so that he wouldn't leave clues. Why would he send one now? Believe me, they'll find a parachute, a body and a bag of dollars."

"You just don't like admitting you could be wrong," the stewardess teased her captain.

Eight years after the theft, a deer hunter found a metal notice from the Boeing plane. It said, "This hatch must remain closed in flight."

There was a rush of treasure-hunters to the mountains looking for the ransom money from that hijack. They practically trampled the mountains flat. No parachute and no body was ever found . . . but a man and his eight-year-old son discovered a bundle of weather-worn banknotes.

"I always said they'd find the money," Bill Scott gloated.

"You always said they'd find a parachute, a body and a bag of dollars," she reminded him.

"One out of three ain't bad," Bill Scott grumbled.

"And that's all it will ever be," Tina said. "Mr D. B. Cooper has vanished like the Invisible Man."

Invisible thief — Make up your mind

Most hijackers are despised criminals. They bring the threat of mass death to a plane-load of innocent men, women and children. Yet, for some reason, D. B. Cooper became a sort of hero to Americans during the 1970s. His story was told and re-told in many newspapers and magazines. His famous letter insisted that he was no Robin Hood, yet that's just how many people saw him. After the letter was published . . .

- *His name was sprayed over posters throughout America*
- *T-shirts were printed with his name*
- *Disc jockeys played records for him on their radio shows*
- *Young women swore they would marry him if he was ever found*

But did he survive the jump? Examine some of the facts . . .

1. People who knew the woods believed that no one could survive there without food or warm clothing. Even his pursuers had trouble getting into the forests to search properly. One badly equipped man would have found it harder to get out of them . . . or impossible.

2. Expert parachutists believed only a skilled jumper could have survived the drop. There were 'smoke jumpers' in the Forestry Service fire-fighting team who could have managed it. Each one of these men was checked out – none of them could have been D. B. Cooper.

3. The money that was eventually found had been washed down in a mountain stream. It is possible that Cooper landed in a river and drowned under the weight of the parachute. This would explain why his body was never found in the woods.

4. The ransom money handed over to Cooper was secretly marked. As none of it ever turned up in banks it was almost certainly never spent.

But . . .

1. Law officers searched with helicopters but no parachute was ever located – such a large expanse of white silk would have been spotted easily. So, it's possible D. B. Cooper survived the jump and was therefore able to to fold-up his parachute.

2. The Air Force used heat-seeking detectors which are capable of finding bodies – they found nothing.

3. Thousands of people have spent countless hours on 'Cooper's Loot' weekend hunts. They have found nothing except the hatch sign and the $3,000.

4. D. B. Cooper had planned every detail of the hijack. He knew the mechanics of the Boeing 727, he knew about airport workings and he was familiar with

the methods the law uses in dealing with hijacks. It's unlikely he'd be so stupid as to jump out of the plane unless he knew exactly where he'd land.

There is one other theory that has been considered that certainly fits all the facts: The idea that the crew of the Boeing 727 were part of the plot . . .

1. The crew bought a ticket in the name of D. B. Cooper but no one of that name actually got on the plane. They then told ground control that Cooper had a bomb. The FBI delivered the money and the passengers were released. (Remember, no passengers ever saw a man with a bomb.)

2. The plane took off.

3. The crew announced that Cooper had jumped – it would suit them to pick a spot which was difficult to survive in. They threw out a few thousand dollars to back up their story, but shared out the rest.

4. They landed and told the D. B. Cooper story. They sent the letter to the FBI three weeks later to back up their story. They then discovered that the money was marked. They could never spend it.

The FBI, of course, checked out this story and the crew were never blamed.

Many see D. B. Cooper as a hero. They would very much like to believe he survived. What do you think?

4. Mystery of the Guardian Angel

Are there such things as angels? Many religions such as Islam and Christianity believe that there are. They believe that everyone has a Guardian Angel to look after them. There are so many stories about strange happenings that they cannot all be imagined, can they? And some experiences seem to prove that there are more things in heaven and earth than we can ever explain . . .

London, England – 1963

The looking glass was old. As old as the house itself. No one could remember where it had come from. Perhaps it had always been there.

When the Henson family moved in it was there. It was in the room they decided would be just right for young Jenny. A bright room that overlooked Hampstead Heath. A room Jenny soon filled with her toys, her books and her doll's house. A room she felt at home in. It felt like she'd always lived there. Just as the looking glass had always lived there.

"I like this room," her friend Suzie said as they sat playing one day. Usually they played outside on the Heath, but today it was raining and they had pulled out an old jigsaw to amuse themselves.

"It's a magical room," Jenny said.

"Oh, yes?" Suzie replied. "My father says there's no such thing as magic."

Her friend sighed. "I know. My mum says the same thing. But that mirror is definitely magical. There's a girl who lives in it."

Suzie looked at her. Was this a game Jenny wanted her to play? Or was she serious? Jenny didn't sound as if she was making it up. She sounded quite matter-of-fact. "You mean like that 'Alice through the Looking Glass' book? Miss Marshall read us some of that last year. It was a nice story."

"Oh, this isn't a story," Jenny told her. "It's true. There's a girl living inside the mirror. I call her Alice because of the story . . . but I don't know if that's her real name."

"What does she look like?" Suzie asked.

"Oh, long blond hair, blue eyes, about our age."

Suzie laughed. "That's your reflection, you dummy!"

Jenny frowned. "No, it can't be. She isn't there when I look into the mirror. I see her when I'm lying in bed. I wake up and look at the mirror and I see her watching me."

"Probably dreaming," her friend said.

"I'm as awake as you are now," Jenny said

46

patiently.

"So what does this girl say to you?"

"Oh, she doesn't speak . . . she's behind the glass. I don't think she wants to speak to me. She just wants to watch over me."

"Maybe she's your guardian angel," Suzie suggested.

Jenny shook her head. "Doesn't look like an angel. Doesn't have wings and white robes and a harp and things. She just has a dress on – an old-fashioned sort of dress."

"Maybe she's the spirit of the girl that used to live in this room."

"That's what I thought," Jenny agreed.

"So aren't you scared?"

"Not at all. It's more like having a friend."

"I'm your friend, aren't I?" Suzie asked.

"You're my best friend," Jenny said. "But it's nice to know Alice is there behind the looking glass."

Suzie walked over to the mirror and stared deep into it. All she could see was a round, cheerful face looking back at her. The face was framed by short brown hair. She put her tongue out and her reflection showed its pink tongue. "Alice!" she called. "Is there anybody there?"

"Nobody else has seen her except me," Jenny explained. "I think that's why they don't believe me. But you believe me, don't you, Suzie?"

The brown-haired girl ran her fingers over the carved wooden frame that was covered with fine gold leaf. She felt a slight tingle as she touched it. "Yes, Jen. I believe you."

That winter was bitterly cold and the girls spent many hours playing in the room. The Christmas holidays arrived and Jenny was wrapping Suzie's present when the telephone rang. Mrs Henson took the call on the kitchen telephone then came into the living room carrying a handful of tinsel for the tree. "That was Mrs Bergman," she said. "Suzie can't come over to play with you today."

"That's not fair," Jenny moaned.

"I don't mean her mother won't let her," Mrs Henson said. "I mean she's too poorly."

Jenny pulled a face of disappointment. "She's only got a cold."

"Don't be so selfish, Jenny. Think of someone else for a change. Suzie's always had a weak chest. That cold has turned into a fever. Mrs Bergman was so worried she called in the doctor."

"Will she be all right?" Jenny asked guiltily.

"She's off to the chemist's now to pick up a prescription. Once Suzie gets the tablets she should be fine."

Jenny stood up and walked across to the living-room window. "Can we get her a get well soon card?"

Mrs Henson began untangling the Christmas tree lights. "It's freezing out there. I don't really want to go out unless I have to. Why not go up to your room and make a card for Suzie?"

Jenny brightened up. "All right," she agreed and hurried up to the room to find her coloured pencils. As she sat at her dressing table drawing, Jenny began chatting to the mirror. Alice wasn't visible. She only seemed to come at night. But Jenny felt she was there, listening. "I'm making a card for Suzie. She's poorly," she explained to the looking glass. Then the girl stopped and looked up. She looked at her own reflection. "I've never been poorly since we moved into this house, have I? Maybe you are my guardian angel after all. I think it's Suzie who needs you," she smiled and went back to work.

The card was soon finished and Mrs Henson promised her daughter that she could take it round to Suzie's house the next day. "No point putting it in the Christmas post. By the time it gets there she'll be better."

Jenny nodded and placed the card on the mantelpiece, then set about helping with the tree and mixing the Christmas pudding. The freezing wind dropped a little later in the afternoon and she went out with her mother to do some shopping. By nine o'clock she was exhausted. "I'm off to bed, Mum," she said.

"Sleep tight, mind the fleas don't bite," Mrs Henson said.

Jenny climbed into bed wearily and glanced across at the mirror. It reflected the curtains at the window. The orange of the street lights made them glow warmly. Jenny fell into a deep sleep.

She didn't know what woke her. The clock at her bedside said ten o'clock. The curtains flickered white as cars drove past with their headlights on. She turned and looked the other way. Alice was looking at her through the mirror.

"Hello, Alice!" she said. "What's wrong?"

The shadowy reflection looked troubled. She was raising her pale hands to the mirror and pushing at the glass. Jenny sat up in bed. She strained her eyes in the darkness to see what Alice was doing. She felt a thrill of excitement as the looking-glass girl pushed one shadowy hand through the glass, then another. Her head followed and finally her body. She stood on the rug in front of the empty mirror. Her lips began to move and Jenny heard a voice echoing in the room.

"It's Suzie," the voice said.

Jenny jumped out of bed. The movement alarmed Alice and she stepped back towards the looking glass. "No! Don't come near. You mustn't ever touch."

"Sorry," Jenny said quickly and sat on the edge of her bed. "What about Suzie?"

"She is ill . . ." the voice said.

"I know. She's got a cold."

"No-o . . . the doctor gave her tablets to help her sleep. She has taken too many. She will never wake up. Warn her! Warn her!" The voice grew fainter as if it had used up all its strength. The figure faded too and seemed to shrink as it slid back into the mirror and disappear.

Jenny jumped to her feet. "Alice?" she cried. "Alice!" There was no reply. The girl didn't wait to find her slippers or dressing gown but ran to her door and leapt down the stairs two at a time. She was breathless as she burst into the living room. "Mum! It's Suzie! She's ill. Terribly ill! You have to get the doctor!"

Mrs Henson gripped her daughter's shoulders and sat her down firmly in an armchair. "Calm down,

Jenny. You've had a bad dream."

"No! I saw Alice . . ."

"Exactly. One of your dreams. Now get back to bed and I'll make you some hot milk."

Jenny tried to object and poured out her story of Alice in the looking glass. Mrs Henson listened, tight-lipped. "No, Jenny, I will not phone Mrs Bergman with this silly story. Now get back to bed and I'll be up in five minutes."

Jenny looked at her mother's stern expression and knew she would never persuade her in time. She had to think of something. Something very quickly.

"Yes, Mum. Sorry, Mum. Don't worry about the milk. I've disturbed you watching that programme. I'll make it myself."

Mrs Henson sighed and settled back into her chair. "You're too old to be telling these fairy stories, Jenny."

"Yes, Mum," the girl agreed and slipped out of the door. The tiles were cold on her feet as she tipped a cup of milk into a pan and turned the gas ring on. Then she climbed onto a stool and lifted down the telephone receiver. There was a 'ting' of the telephone bell. The girl waited to see if her mother had heard it. She decided the television had drowned out the noise.

Jenny dialled the number carefully and heard it ring at the other end. "Mrs Bergman? It's Jenny Henson here."

"What are you doing out of bed at this time of night?"

"I . . . I was worried about Suzie."

"Nothing to worry about there. The doctor gave her

some tablets and she's sound asleep . . . and that's where you should be!"

"But what would happen if she took too many tablets?"

There was a long silence on the other end of the line. Finally Mrs Bergman said, "Suzie wouldn't do that."

"But she might . . . can't you check?"

"Now listen, young Jenny, you have some very silly ideas in your head. Get yourself back to bed at once." And there was a clatter as the phone was replaced firmly at the other end.

Tears began to sting the girl's eyes as she slipped her feet down to the cold floor. She tipped the warm milk into a cup and carried it back up to bed.

The mirror looked strangely quiet now. At rest. Jenny too felt easier. She'd done her best. Maybe the grown-ups were right after all. With the warm milk and the easy mind she slipped back into sleep.

It was almost eleven o'clock when she opened her eyes again. The telephone ringing downstairs had woken her. Five minutes later her bedroom door creaked open. Mrs Henson stood uncertainly in the doorway. "Jenny?" she called softly.

"Yes, Mum? I'm awake. I heard the telephone."

"That was Mrs Bergman."

"Is Suzie all right?" Jenny asked and sat up quickly. Her mother lowered herself onto the edge of the bed and stroked her daughter's hair.

"You phoned Mrs Bergman an hour ago."

Jenny felt her face glowing hot. "Sorry, Mum. I was worried and I . . ."

52

"No, no. Listen," Mrs Henson said. Jenny was surprised that she didn't sound too annoyed. "Mrs Bergman thought you were being silly . . . just like I thought you were being silly. She went back to reading her book. She couldn't concentrate. You'd put that idea of the tablets into her head and she was worried."

"Sorry, Mum, I didn't mean to scare her," Jenny mumbled miserably

"I know, I know. But she couldn't settle until she'd looked in on Suzie again. She went upstairs to Suzie's room and checked. She was asleep . . . but she wasn't snoring the way she usually did when she had that cold. She was in a deep, deep sleep. Mrs Bergman went and looked at the bottle of tablets in the bathroom. The bottle was empty. Suzie must have sneaked out of bed and taken the rest of them."

"Why?" Jenny cried.

"Maybe she thought that if one tablet would cure her slowly then a whole bottle would cure her quickly . . . quickly enough for Christmas."

"Will she die?" Jenny asked.

Mrs Henson gripped her daughter's hand and said, "No . . . but she would have done. She would have done if you hadn't made that phone call to Mrs Bergman. You saved your friend's life, Jenny. I don't know how, but you saved Suzie's life."

Jenny looked over her mother's shoulder. The mirror reflected the curtains at the window and the curtains glowed with the warm orange light. "No I didn't, Mum. No I didn't. Our guardian angel did."

Guardian angels — what do you think?

Jenny's vision sounds incredible – and nobody else ever saw "Alice" – but how else do you explain the phone call that saved her friend's life? Her parents were so amazed that they repeated the story to the local newspapers even though it could have led to Jenny being cruelly treated as a freak.

Over the years there have been many examples of people receiving messages from strange apparitions which later proved to be true . . .

1. England, 1856
A girl was walking home along a quiet country road when the road seemed to disappear for a few moments. The girl saw a vision in front of her. The image was of the white room in her own house. In the middle of the room her mother lay collapsed on the floor. Instead of going home she went straight to the doctor and persuaded him to come home with her. They found the girl's mother, collapsed on the floor in the white room. They arrived just in time to save her.

2. The Atlantic Ocean, 1928
A German sailor, Franz Romer, set sail on a solo voyage from Europe to America. A storm threw him off course and he was lost. He thought he would just sail ahead till the weather cleared but in the middle of the night he heard a voice. The voice told him to turn sharply to the south. He obeyed the voice though he could see no one. The next morning he checked his

charts and discovered his position. If he hadn't obeyed the voice then he would have sailed straight onto some deadly rocks.

3. France, 1915
Captain Terence Bayliss was killed fighting during the First World War in March 1915. In September of that year his troops went into another battle. They were under heavy fire from enemy positions and wanted to turn back. Suddenly, a British officer on a white horse appeared and waved the men forward. The shells and bullets flew but not one touched the officer on the horse. The men obeyed and went forward. They achieved a great victory, but could see nothing of the officer who had guided them to safety. The troops were sure that the man on the horse was Captain Bayliss.

4. Canada, 1949
Two Canadian Mounted Policemen (Mounties) were patrolling on their dog-sled and were caught in a blizzard. They were a long way from shelter and night was falling. The track ahead was covered and they soon became lost. They faced a grim death in the bitter wind. Then a huge figure raced past them on a sledge drawn by white huskies. They called to him but he ignored them. They followed his trail anyway and it led them to safety. When they arrived at the outpost there was no sign of the man. But the locals said they had seen the spirit of Esau Dillingham – a man who had died thirty years before, but who had since led hundreds to safety.

5. Philadelphia, USA, 1979

Mrs Tillotson lived in an apartment building opposite her daughter, Helen. One night she woke up to hear Helen knocking on her door and calling. She opened the door to see her daughter disappearing down the stairs and across the road. She followed. When she reached her daughter's apartment the door was closed. She knocked. "Why did you ask me to follow you?" she asked. "I didn't. I've been asleep in bed all night," Helen replied. "I saw you and heard you!" Mrs Tillotson said. At that moment there was an explosion as a gas leak blasted Mrs Tillotson's apartment. If it hadn't been for her daughter's apparition leading her to safety then she would certainly have died.

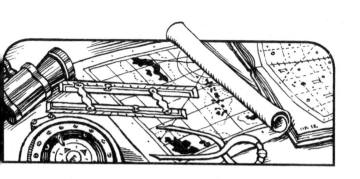

5. Mystery of the Vanishing Plane

Some mysteries are easily solved. But some of the world's greatest mysteries grow even greater with time. Just when you think you have the answer some new evidence comes along that makes you ask, "Is that what really happened?" . . .

The Pacific Ocean – 1937

Whatever happened to Amelia? It's sixty years since she vanished yet people still talk about the mystery of her disappearance.

Of course, she was an American heroine. Throughout the years her stories have filled page after page of newspapers. Her greatest adventure began in 1937 and readers queued at the newspaper stands for the latest account of her exploits.

This is how the newspapers described her most amazing adventure in 1937:

Amelia out to beat the world!

Fearless flier, Amelia Earhart has announced her plan for the most daring adventure ever undertaken by a woman. Brave Amelia plans to be the first person – man or woman – to fly round the world by the longest route: straight around the Equator.

American heroine Amelia already has a string of records under her belt. Back in 1928 she became the first woman to fly across the Atlantic Ocean. Not satisfied with being a passenger – a "piece of baggage" as she described it – she was back three years later to fly herself across the ocean, solo.

Amelia (38), married to publisher George Putnam, has made many flights since then but never been able to find a challenge to match that Atlantic crossing. Now she has it. The lively lady will set out from California in June. She'll be flying an all-American twin-engine Lockheed Electra and will take along ace navigator Fred Noonan to plot the record route.

Plucky Amelia once nurtured ambitions to become a nurse. Now she'll be nursing that 600-horsepower aircraft over the Atlantic Ocean and the even wider Pacific. All America will have its fingers crossed for their favourite flier.

But later that year readers were horrified by the next headline they read:

13 May 1937

Amelia Crashes!

Reports are coming in from Honolulu that brave bird-woman Amelia Earhart has crashed on the latest leg of her round-the-world flight. The record-breaking flight would make her the first flier ever to circle the globe. The crash has damaged the plane but early reports say Amelia and navigator Fred Noonan are not hurt. It is believed she will try again later this year. Husband, wealthy publisher George Putnam, said he had no details of the accident yet but was sure his brave wife would battle on.

The nation held its breath until it was confirmed that Amelia was safe. Then, within a month, the adventure began again.

2 June 1937

Up and away for Amelia!

Amelia Earhart's awesome adventure got underway today. She set off from Oakland, California on the first leg of a journey that will take her round the world – the long way! Amelia will fly to Miami, Brazil, Dakar, Khartoum, Rangoon, Singapore, Darwin and New Guinea before returning to the United States in time for 4th of July celebrations.

The 27,000 mile journey is the most dangerous anyone could imagine. The plucky lady will cross pitiless deserts, towering mountain ranges and vast oceans where one small mistake could cost her life. Spectators waving Amelia off at Oakland all agreed, if anyone can do it that gutsy American girl can.

Newspaper and radio reports let Amelia's fans track her progress around the world. It seemed she was heading for one of the biggest parties America had ever seen when they reported:

2 July 1937

Homeward Bound Amelia

Amelia Earhart sets out on the last lap of her phenomenal round-the-world flight today . . . and once more into the record books! She flies the Pacific Ocean from Lae (in New Guinea) to Howland Island. A 2,556 mile journey over open water that no one has ever attempted before.

"This is the big one," her manager Bob Francis said as he charted her progress back in California. "Howland Island is a tiny speck of land to find in all that water! Let's hope navigator Fred Noonan is spot on with his calculations. Not a lot of ships use that route so they'd better not hit the water."

Of course the US Coast Guard ship Itasca is waiting at Howland for her. It's rumoured that the Itasca has the very latest direction-finding equipment. The US Navy aren't saying too much about this top-secret radio system but Amelia did have talks with the US government before setting off.

Reports of Fred Noonan having some problems with his navigation chronometers were described as "exaggerated" by Amelia's manager. The weather was clear though they'll be flying into a strong headwind which will slow them down. Weather forecasts were for storms ahead. "Amelia will fly over them," Francis said. "Ain't nothing going to stop her now."

Of course true adventures, like true love, never run smoothly! The people back home were disappointed at the reports the next day. Disappointed, but not too worried at the story which read . . .

3 July 1937

Amelia hitch

Amelia Earhart, round-the-world air ace, was due to land at Howland Island in mid Pacific at 6:30 a.m. First reports suggest she's been delayed. Strong headwinds are the probable cause. Coastguards on Howland have received radio messages from the Lockheed Electra asking for assistance. The US ship Itasca is believed to have the latest equipment on board. "We should be able to pinpoint her, wherever she is, and guide her down to Howland," the captain said yesterday before she set off. He was not available for comment this morning.

All America is praying for that magical message, "Landed safely on Howland."

But that disappointment turned to real fear when that

"Landed safely" message failed to come through. There is a saying, "No news is good news." Soon people had stopped believing that. America should have been celebrating Independence Day. Instead they were talking about only one thing. As the newspapers said . . .

4 July 1937

Amelia – Fears grow

Independence Day celebrations are strangely subdued across the United States today as people have just one question on their minds. Where is air adventurer Amelia Earhart?

She was last heard from at 8:45 a.m. yesterday morning, as she attempted to find tiny Howland Island in the Pacific. Her last message complained of windy conditions and navigation problems because of cloud cover. She was heard begging for assistance. After that the Lockheed Electra must certainly have ditched into the sea from lack of fuel. The US Pacific Fleet is steaming to the area on a search mission. Angry Americans are asking, why did the new direction-finding equipment on board the ship Itasca fail? The cruel and simple answer seems to be that the batteries had run down.

Now the nation was in mourning. They didn't want to believe their idol was dead. They clutched at any news to give them hope. They even wanted to hear wildly unlikely stories. Stories like . . .

10 July 1937

"Amelia alive" says air pioneer

As the US Navy continues to search the Pacific for lost pilot Amelia Earhart, another famed female flier claims she knows that Amelia is safe! Jacqueline Cochrane is not only a skilled pilot in the same class as Amelia Earhart. She also has psychic powers which have told her that the Lockheed Electra is afloat and Amelia is alive.

"Navigator Noonan is also alive, but badly injured," Jacqueline claims. The spooky story is backed up by amateur radio operators who say they have received SOS calls which could well come from the Electra. Joe Bentini of San Francisco said, "They were clear at first. That suggests an experienced operator like Noonan. Then they became more confused. I guess Noonan died or maybe he leapt into the shark-infested waters to lighten the sinking plane. I'm afraid I couldn't quite pinpoint the signals – but they were somewhere in the mid-Pacific."

There's nothing quite so cruel as false hope. Two weeks after Amelia's disappearance the heartbroken people of America were having to face the bitter truth about their heroine.

19 July 1937

Amelia – Search called off

The search for lost heroine Amelia Earhart has been called off. The US Navy finally admitted defeat. "If she did ditch the plane then she wouldn't survive without water," Admiral Keegan said in Washington today. The search cost US taxpayers $4,000,000 but no one is complaining. "Some day we may come across the plane and find out what really happened," the admiral said.

Last night Amelia's husband George Putnam revealed the contents of her final letter to him. It read: "Please know that I am quite aware of the hazards. I want to do it – because I want to do it. Women must try to do things that men have tried. If they fail then their failure must be a challenge to others." Mr Putnam said that Amelia once told him, "If I have to go then I'd like to go in my plane. Quickly." It looks like she may have had her wish.

The Navy closed the most painful chapter in its glorious history with three short words. Lost at sea. America is in mourning for its greatest heroine.

And that should have been that. In time the sadness over Amelia's disappearance was forgotten. After all, by 1939, there was a great war in Europe to worry about. By late 1941 America had joined that war.

It was a world war and America was battling against Japan. The battleground was the very area where Amelia had disappeared. Then, on September 14, came a sensational story that put the forgotten flier right back on the front pages . . .

9 September 1944

Earhart crash claim!

American Marines captured Marshall Island in the Pacific today. The Japanese Island was taken in some of the fiercest fighting of the war so far. The US Marines were welcomed by people and told a strange story.

It seems that seven years ago the Japanese had two fliers as prisoners – a man and a woman. The woman died of dysentery and the man was executed as a spy. July 1937 was just the time American flier Amelia Earhart and navigator Fred Noonan disappeared in the Pacific. US military chiefs are refusing to comment on the suggestion that Earhart was not flying to Howland Island, 500 miles to the south-east. That she was in fact on a spying mission to photograph Japanese defences in the event of a war. It seems possible that Earhart's Lockheed plane was shot down by Japanese fighters and the Americans died in captivity. That would certainly solve the mystery of her disappearance.

The war in the Pacific was still going on in 1945 and the new stories about Amelia Earhart continued to trickle back to America.

17 June 1945

Earhart mystery deepens

Claims that Amelia Earhart was spying on Japanese defences when she disappeared eight years ago were backed up by shock new evidence today. US Army officials have always denied the popular woman aviator was captured by the Japanese and died a prisoner. But following the magnificent US victory at Okinawa Island in the Pacific, marines searching the clothing of Japanese victims came across a strange item in the pocket of one man. He was carrying a photograph of Amelia Earhart. Is this proof that she was once a Japanese prisoner?

But nothing more was found. Again the memories of Amelia faded. For over forty years investigators followed up the war-time stories but uncovered very little. Just when it seemed the file on Amelia Earhart would be closed forever there was an announcement that woke up the old memories . . .

12 August 1989

Amelia Earhart – The truth?

The International Group for Historic Aviation Recovery have spent several years trying to trace the wreckage of Amelia Earhart's ill-fated Lockheed Electra. They finally homed in on Nikumaroro – five hundred miles south of her destination, Howland

Island. They found several objects including a cigarette lighter and a 1930s aircraft battery. They believe that Earhart and her navigator may have become lost and crash-landed on Nikumaroro Island rather than ditch in the sea. They could have survived several days before dying of thirst. Investigations are continuing.

The mystery of Amelia Earhart was alive again. More efforts were put into the investigation and they were rewarded in 1992 when fresh reports claimed . . .

13 March 1992

Amelia Earhart – Found at last?

A second expedition to Nikumaroro Island in the Pacific has unearthed some important clues to the 55-year-old mystery of Amelia Earhart's disappearance. Searchers came across the size 9 sole and heel of a "Cat's Paw" shoe – the type and size that Amelia Earhart was wearing when she was last seen. They also found a section of a 1930s aircraft with Lockheed riveting – and it was a Lockheed that the American woman was flying. The cap from a bottle proved to be from a medicine bottle; it was the type of bottle that held a stomach treatment Amelia was taking. The Director of the International Group for Historic Aviation Recovery, Richard Gillespie, is convinced the mystery of her disappearance is now solved. Of course finding the plane does not truly solve the greater mystery – how did the world's greatest flier come to be five hundred miles off course?

And this mystery story is still alive today. Until a final explanation is found you will have to examine the reports – and the following facts – and make up your own mind.

The vanishing plane —Fact file

Some day someone may come up with absolute proof of Amelia Earhart's fate. Many books and articles have been written about the mystery – very few agree about the true solution. Most clues suggest that it was simply bad organisation and poor navigating that caused her to lose her way and be forced to land in the sea or on an unsuitable island.

Look at the facts . . .

Fred Noonan was described as an expert navigator. The truth is he was being treated for the problem of drinking too much alcohol. The round-the-world trip was part of his cure. But even the world's best navigators would have had trouble finding that tiny island in the largest ocean on earth – an island of 2 square miles in an ocean of 64 million square miles.

The two should not have set off at all on that part of the journey. The problem with the navigation instruments had not been fixed and the weather was too windy and too cloudy. Even in perfect weather it was a dangerous journey – in bad weather it was suicidal. Amelia Earhart was simply impatient.

The plane had no spare radio and no distress rockets. They were not equipped for an emergency like a forced landing because they didn't think it could happen to them. (Rather like the Titanic *setting sail without enough lifeboats.*)

The radio links with the US ships were poor. The Itasca *sent out signals to help contact the fliers. But* the aircraft signals were too short and faint for the ship to find them. When the Lockheed Electra went down the Itasca sailed around Howland Island looking for it. In fact they were just guessing. The plane could well have come down 500 miles away as the findings of the 1980s suggest.

The flight was so badly planned that some people have said it had to be a deliberate accident. Amelia Earhart was sent by the US government to crash land on a Japanese island. Even though the Second World War had not started, the Japanese build-up of forces made a war in the Pacific likely. How could the US fly over Japanese islands and spy on them? Say they were searching for Amelia Earhart! There are a few facts to back up this wild idea . . . including the fact that the US government still refuses to open its records on the mystery to the public!

6. Mystery of the Mary Celeste

Some mysteries will never be solved. But they continue to interest people for that very reason. And inevitably, as time goes by, the truth becomes buried beneath the many retellings of the tale . . .

The Atlantic Ocean – 1872*

"The mystery of the *Mary Celeste*? Hah! There's no mystery!" Captain David Moorhouse sneered and buried his nose in his mug of ale. The tavern was crowded and the air was thick with yellow pipe smoke. Ale flowed off the dark oak tables and onto the sawdust on the floor.

The captain kept the mug to his lips but raised his tired eyes to the young man opposite. "I've been asked to write an article for the *Daily Echo* and I thought you'd be able to help."

The captain lowered his drink at last and wiped his moustache on his sleeve. "You're not the first to ask

*Date *Mary Celeste* found abandoned

and I dare say you won't be the last. Look, I'll tell you what I'll do. I'll tell you the story – the full story – for a guinea."

"Oh, yes," the young reporter said eagerly and he pulled a pencil from his pocket and a small notebook. He wrote '*Marie Celeste*' at the top and looked up. The old sailor was glaring at him. "The ship was called Mary not Marie. Some writers changed the name in their reports. I suppose they thought Marie sounds a bit more unusual for such a strange story. The truth is she was just plain old Mary . . . at least she was when I found her. Of course, when she was launched she had another name."

"Really, Captain Moorhouse?" the young reporter said. "I didn't know that."

"You don't know much, Mr . . ."

"Baxter . . . Albert Baxter."

"Well, Mr Baxter, the first thing you can tell your readers is the *Mary Celeste* was launched in 1860 under the name *The Amazon*. And from the time she was launched she was a cursed ship."

"Do you believe that?" the reporter asked as he scribbled.

Captain Moorhouse leaned forward, "What else could you call it?" he said. "Her first captain was put in charge . . . and he died three days later. On her first voyage she hit a fishing boat and was damaged. As she was being repaired a fire broke out. So they sacked the second captain and appointed a third – she hit another ship in the English Channel. They sacked the third captain and hired a fourth. He managed to run her aground and the wreck put the owners out of business."

"But she was repaired."

"Aye, and re-named. Maybe they thought the new name would bring her luck. It didn't. The new owner went bankrupt soon after he bought her."

"And that's when Captain Briggs bought her?" the reporter asked.

"Get your facts right, boy. A company called J. H. Winchester bought her and made Benjamin Briggs captain. They gave him a one-third share of the *Mary Celeste*. He was a good choice. A fine sailor. One of the curious things about the story is that I had dinner with Ben Briggs in September of 1872 . . . less than a month before he sailed."

"And that's why the court thought you were mixed up with his disappearance?" Albert Baxter asked.

"It didn't help," Captain Moorhouse said sourly. "Anyway, that was the last I ever saw of him. I crossed the Atlantic and was on the way back to America when we sighted a ship about five miles from us. Have you ever seen a dead man, Mr Baxter?" he asked suddenly.

"Why, yes . . . once," the young man said and stopped writing.

"What we saw was a dead ship. It's just as sickening. Only two of her sails were set – the others were in tatters. She was staggering from starboard to port and back again as if her steersman was drunk. But as we got nearer we realised we couldn't see anyone at the wheel of the ship. We couldn't see anyone anywhere. She looked deserted. Then we came round the stern of the ship and I saw her name

– *Mary Celeste*! I knew it was Ben Briggs's ship and I felt a terrible fear that something had happened to him."

The reporter sucked at his pencil and began writing again. "So you climbed on board the *Mary Celeste* did you, Captain Moorhouse?"

"Me? No!" the man snapped. "I had my own ship to command. I sent my first mate, Oliver Deveaux, and two crew men to investigate. It took them about an hour to investigate and then they returned."

"What did they find, Captain Moorhouse?" Albert Baxter asked eagerly.

"Ah, that's what they all want to know. And it's the wrong question!" the sailor exploded. "You should be asking what they didn't find, Mr Baxter. What they didn't find is just as important."

"So what didn't they find?"

"They didn't find the lifeboat, Mr Baxter."

"But I thought . . ."

"I know, I know, I know! There were stories that the lifeboat was still in place and that made a real mystery of it. But believe me, Mr Baxter, there was no lifeboat on the *Mary Celeste* when we found her."

"Ah," the reporter said, "but did she have one when she set sail?"

"Of course. I mean, the old ship's curse was still holding true. When they were loading barrels in New York they dropped one and smashed the longboat. But Ben Briggs wouldn't have set sail without one. He had another lifeboat on board and decided that was enough."

"For thirteen crew?"

"Mr Baxter, Mr Baxter! Will you get your facts right. There were not unlucky thirteen on board the *Mary Celeste* like the stories say. There was Captain Briggs, his wife Sarah, their two-year-old daughter Sophie and seven crew. That makes ten . . . at least it did when I went to school."

"Thank you. But is it true about the bloodstained sword?" Albert Baxter asked.

"They found the sword under the captain's bed," the sailor said impatiently. "It was an antique. And there were stains on the blade. The story went around that they were blood stains. That's what went in the news reports back in 1872. The truth was they were rust stains – the newspapers forgot to print that because it wasn't so exciting!"

"No blood?"

"Ah, I didn't say that. There were stains on the rail at the side of the deck . . . and those stains were of blood. Deveaux reported them. He also reported that the ship had been abandoned in a great hurry. He was shaken by what he'd seen. He didn't want to sail the *Mary Celeste* back to Gibraltar. In the end I persuaded him."

"So the authorities could investigate?" the reporter asked.

The captain looked at him with pity. "For the money, Mr Baxter. It's called salvage. Rescue an abandoned ship and you get a reward."

"And you got the reward?"

Captain Moorhouse frowned. "We were treated like criminals. The investigators made all sorts of wild claims. Said we could have plotted with Ben Briggs to abandon his own vessel and claim the salvage money. Crazy! Absolutely crazy. But they gave us a pitiful amount of salvage money – £1700 – to make sure we didn't profit from any crooked deals."

"But what do you think happened, Captain Moorhouse?" Albert Baxter asked.

The sailor drained his beer and reached for a jug to re-fill his mug. "The answer lay in a short piece of rope. It was hanging over the side of the *Mary Celeste* and it had snapped. We believed that was a tow rope. Ben Briggs and his crew had gone into the lifeboat and let the *Mary Celeste* tow them along."

"Why would they do that?" the reporter asked.

Captain Moorhouse looked pleased with himself. "Exactly. Something happened which made Ben think the ship was going to sink. So they got into the lifeboat just to be on the safe side. They wanted to see which way the *Mary Celeste* would go. There was no cooked food on the ship – they must have taken it all with them in case they were in for a long stay in the lifeboat. And the navigation instruments were missing – in case they had to find their way to the nearest land. But that rope shows they were hoping to get back on the ship. Then the rope snapped – they had to watch helplessly as the *Mary Celeste* disappeared over the horizon!"

"So what happened to make them abandon ship?"

"My men found some of the cargo damaged – casks of pure alcohol. If those casks had leaked then the alcohol could have exploded and thrown the hatch covers off. There'd be clouds of smoke. It would look like a disastrous fire. That's about the only thing that would panic a good seaman like Ben Briggs."

"I see . . . but how do you explain the warm cup of tea and the hot meal on the table when your men boarded her."

Captain Moorhouse rubbed his eyes tiredly. "For goodness sake, Mr Baxter, can we stick to the facts? There was no warm tea or hot meal. There was some writer called Conan Doyle: he wrote the story of the *Mary Celeste* twenty years after we found her. He wrote it as if he was a survivor – a great story, Mr Baxter – but no more real than *Alice in Wonderland*. Unfortunately some newspapers published the story as if it was true."

Albert Baxter wrote his notes patiently. "No hot tea and no hot meal."

"And no mystery . . . just a very sad story," the captain sighed. "Imagine being adrift in the Atlantic Ocean in winter with a two-year-old baby and a woman. A slow, cold death, Mr Baxter. And that's the truth."

Albert Baxter folded his notebook and reached into his pocket for a sovereign. He pushed it across the table to the captain. The man looked at it then picked it up. "Of course you could write about the curse. Do you know how the *Mary Celeste* finished up?"

"No," the reporter said.

"She didn't last ten years after we found her. In the end a captain drove her onto rocks. Wrecked her to claim the insurance."

"And because of the curse he was caught!" Albert nodded.

"He was found not guilty," the sailor said.

The reporter looked disappointed. "So the *Mary Celeste* wasn't cursed in the end."

"They decided to have another trial – the captain didn't get to the second trial. He died and his partner in the crime died three months later. Old Mary decided that if she was going to die then she'd take another couple of sailors with her. So don't write about the mystery of the *Mary Celeste*, Mr Baxter. Write a story about the curse of the *Mary Celeste*!"

The Mary Celeste — VERDICT

The inquiry into the Mary Celeste *mystery published its findings, but these never caused a great sensation at the time. It was only when the creator of Sherlock Holmes, the writer Conan Doyle, re-told the story as a mystery that public interest was stirred. It was extremely popular and people began to show a great fascination.*

Over the past hundred years many books have been written about the fate of the Mary Celeste. *Some of these ideas have been believable. Some have been hilarious! Make up your own mind . . .*

1. Fire water

One of the owners of the Mary Celeste *heard a story of alcohol exploding at sea and frightening a crew into abandoning their ship. Captain Briggs's own nephew preferred this explanation. The hatches on the deck had been flipped over as if they had been blown off – no sailor would ever leave a hatch upside down as they were found. But . . . the investigators in Gibraltar said they could see no trace of an explosion and rejected it.*

2. Drunk

The Gibraltar investigators did find the barrels of alcohol broken open just as Captain Moorhouse reported. They believed the crew had broken into them, become raging drunk, murdered the captain and his family, then sailed off on another ship. But . . .

why didn't the sailors simply stay with the Mary Celeste *and sail off into hiding?*

3. Waterlogged
A popular theory was that a waterspout hit the Mary Celeste. *They are common in that part of the Atlantic. It would suck off the hatch covers and also suck water into the water pumps. This would make the ship appear to have a dangerous two metres of water in her hold. It could have persuaded Captain Briggs to abandon ship. But . . . Briggs was an experienced sailor and this seems a silly mistake for a such a captain to make.*

4. Deadly triangle
There is an area of the Atlantic known as the Bermuda Triangle where several mysterious disappearances are said to have occurred. They are blamed on strange forces – possibly even alien forces. One theory says the crew were snatched by a flying saucer. But . . . why would the aliens be interested in the crew of the Mary Celeste?

5. Prey to pirates
Many people said that the ship had been overrun by pirates. The Mary Celeste *crew were either kidnapped or killed and thrown overboard. But . . . why were there no signs of a fight on board? And why would the pirates take the longboat and the ship's instruments?*

6. Jaws of death
A school teacher claimed to have found a diary

written by a survivor named Fosdyke who told the story of the mystery fifty years after it happened. He said the captain challenged a member of the crew to a swimming race around the ship. As the rest of the ship's company crowded onto a platform to watch the platform collapsed and sent them all into the jaws of waiting sharks. (Fosdyke clung to a piece of wood and drifted to safety.) But . . . there was no record of a passenger called Fosdyke – and it would be much too cold to survive a swim in the Atlantic in late November.

7. Insane sadness

In 1828 Captain William Stewart of the ship Mary Russell went mad, killed the crew then threw himself over the side. Some people believe this could have happened to Briggs – one idea was that Sarah was playing the ship's piano when the ship rolled, the piano moved and crushed her against the cabin wall. Briggs went mad with unhappiness and did the same as Captain Stewart. But . . . if he was so upset about the death of his beloved wife, would he then kill his dear little daughter Sophie?

8. Cold collision

Just like the Titanic forty years later the Mary Celeste came upon an iceberg. Afraid that it would crush their ship, the crew rowed to the iceberg and climbed onto it for safety. The Mary Celeste sailed off and the iceberg carried the crew to a frosty death. But . . . icebergs that far south are rare – and no one else reported an iceberg in that place at that time.

9. Underwater attack

One further idea is that the ship was attacked by a giant squid or octopus. It used its giant tentacles to snatch the sailors off the deck and eat them. But . . . why didn't it damage any part of the ship . . . and why would it want the ship's papers?

Are any of these believable? Which is most likely? Or do you have a better idea?

7. Mystery of the Zombie

Do you believe in black magic? Are there powerful sorcerers who can control us by casting spells like the wicked witches of our childhood fairy tales? Or are they simply ruthless and greedy people who use drugs to control their victims . . .

L'Estere Village, Haiti – 1982

"You won't remember me," the old man said. "I died a long, long time ago."

The girl smiled, her teeth pearl white against her dark brown skin. "You don't look very dead to me!"

The man said, "No, I don't. That's because I'm alive again now."

They sat on the rough wooden seat outside the village graveyard. The girl's friends drifted down the dusty road from school; they regarded the old man curiously then walked on. A smaller girl in a blue checked dressed stopped. "Who's your friend, Ellie?"

"He says his name is Clairvius Narcisse and he's been dead."

The second girl peered at him. "He doesn't look very dead to me!"

Ellie laughed and clapped her hands. "Hah! Josie! That's just what I said!"

"Is he a ghost?" Josie asked and moved across the seat. "I can't see through him."

"Ask him," Ellie said.

Josie pushed her short nose towards the old man. "Are you a ghost, Mr Narcisse?"

The old man shook his head. "No. But I was a Zombie."

"Ah," little Josie said, nodding wisely. "He was a Zombie, Ellie. My father's told me all about Zombies. But I didn't believe him." She turned to the old man. "A *bokor* magician stole your spirit and made you his slave, did he, Mr Narcisse?"

"No, no, no," Clairvius sighed. "There was no voodoo involved in my case; no black magic. Just evil and cunning . . . and drugs. Maybe there are some Zombies out there who have had their spirits stolen. I was not that type of Zombie. Most people who turn into Zombies are the victims of bad people, just like I was."

"So, how were you turned into a Zombie, Mr Narcisse?" Ellie asked.

The old man pointed up the road to the row of houses on the main street. "See that house, third one along on the left?"

The girls nodded.

"That was my house. One of the finest in L'Estere."

"You were rich?" Ellie asked. The man's shirt was clean and white and buttoned up to the collar, but it didn't look like the shirt of a rich man.

"I had my father's house and a good job. I wasn't the richest man in Haiti, but I had plenty," he explained. "Now listen, girls, and listen good. If you have plenty of money then you'll have plenty of something else."

"You'll have plenty of happiness!" Josie put in.

Clairvius looked at her with sad and tired eyes. "Not always, Josie, not always.

"What I was going to say was, you have plenty of *enemies*. There's always someone wants to get their hands on your money. Or someone who's simply jealous that you have something they don't. Always someone who'll do anything they can to get their hands on your money."

"Robbers?" Josie asked, her eyes wide.

"Worse," the old man sighed. "Robbers only take your gold and silver. But the man I'm thinking of took eighteen years of my life. How old are you?" He turned towards the girls.

"I'm thirteen," Ellie said, "and Josie's twelve."

Clairvius nodded. "More years than you've had on earth," he said. "It all happened before you were even born. Back in 1962 it was. I was living in that fine house over there and I had a good business. Then, one night my brother François called to see me. He wanted to borrow some money from me. Just a hundred dollars."

"That's a lot of money," Josie said, wide-eyed. "Did you have that much?"

The old man nodded. "I had that much. But I knew François was a waster. So I offered him fifty dollars. That was when he turned angry and said, 'When you're dead I'll have all of your money, Clairvius.' He stormed out of the house and I never saw him again. But I had an awful feeling in my heart that he meant to harm me."

"He killed you?" Josie asked.

"He got someone else to kill me," Clairvius said. "He sold me to a plantation owner for just twelve dollars. Of course I didn't know that at the time. I was driving along a quiet road when I suddenly got a flat tyre. The spare was flat – though I was sure I'd checked it just a few days before. I was stuck. It was a long way to the nearest garage but a small man with a white beard stepped out of a cottage and said he had a friend who could help. He invited me to have a cup of coffee while we waited."

"That was lucky," Ellie put in.

Clairvius looked down sadly at her. "The man with a white beard was *that* plantation owner."

"Ohhhh!" Ellie said. "Maybe not so lucky."

"There was no *luck* about it," the man sighed. "He had been waiting for me. He caused the puncture. It was just a trick to lure me into his house. First he called a servant with six cracks of his whip. A man walked into the room and I was amazed at his appearance. He was dressed in rags – rags made from sacks. His arms seemed to hang by his sides like an old shirt on a washing line. His skin seemed shrunken onto his bones. But his eyes . . . ah, his eyes. They were deader than a fish. They stared straight ahead but

86

didn't seem to be looking at anything."

"He was a Zombie . . . the walking dead," Ellie said.

Clairvius nodded slowly. "I wasn't as clever as you, young lady. You're right, of course. The poor servant was a Zombie. I should have guessed. I didn't. The plantation owner sent the servant for a pot of coffee and told me the servant was sick. His brain was damaged in an accident. I believed him. Anyway he offered me a mug of coffee."

"And you took it?" Josie gasped.

Old Clairvius sighed. "I took it. It tasted strange but I drank it. Every last drop."

"It was poisoned and you died," Josie said.

The man frowned. "That's what it looked like. First my head felt light and the room began to swim around me. Then I had trouble breathing. My heart felt like it was struggling to beat and my stomach was burning. Then I lost all feeling in my arms and legs. I knew where I was and I could see and hear everything. I could see my host come up to me and stare into my eyes. I could even smell his evil breath. Then he clicked his fingers and the Zombie picked me up. 'Carry him to the side of the car. Lay him down beside the flat tyre. It will look as if he had a heart attack while he was trying to change it,' the man ordered. The Zombie did what he was told and I lay in the sun until an ambulance arrived."

"You'd have been all right once they got you to hospital," Ellie put in. "Teacher says hospitals look after sick people."

Clairvius shook his head. They put me on a

stretcher and carried me off to hospital. A doctor came out to see me. I saw him lift my wrist. He was feeling for my pulse. I heard him say, 'Too late, he's dead.' I wanted to jump up and say, 'I'm not! I'm not!' but I couldn't move. They pulled a sheet over my head and wheeled me off to a dark room. My sister came to see me. I could hear her crying. Then my brother François came. They pulled back the sheet over my face. He looked down at me and I could see the smile on his face. Suddenly I realised that it was François who'd arranged this for me! He'd had me killed and now he was going to get all my money!"

"That's cruel," Ellie said.

"That wasn't the worst!" Clairvius cried. "I had to suffer being put in my coffin. I saw the lid coming down and saw the blackness. I felt myself being carried to the graveyard and lowered into the grave. I could hear the priest speaking and my family crying. Then I heard the worst sound in the world . . . I heard them shovelling the soil over my coffin. Now that should have terrified me, but somehow I just didn't care. I just waited to die . . . but I didn't."

"You stayed there for eighteen years!" Ellie asked.

Clairvius laughed for the first time. "Oh, no. I don't think I stayed there even eighteen hours. The next thing I heard was the earth being shovelled off the coffin then the lid was ripped open. The moonlight flooded in and two pairs of hands dragged me out. I was laid in the back of a truck and covered up. We drove over the bumpiest roads you've ever felt and at last I was lifted out. Even in the moonlight I knew where I was."

"In the plantation owner's cottage," Josie nodded.

"In the plantation owner's cottage," the old man agreed. "They sat me in a chair and the man with the white beard came into the room and spoke to me. 'Ah, Monsieur Narcisse,' he said. 'Once you were a rich man. Now you are a slave. Life can be so unkind.' He laughed a cruel laugh and told me that I was to work in the fields for him. Sowing and weeding and gathering in the harvest. Day after day from sunrise to sunset. Then he gave me something to drink. I had my strength back – I could walk, I could work, but I couldn't think for myself. All I could do was obey orders." The old man shook his head. "It was like having a nightmare and not being able to wake up. I was set to work with other Zombies. Every day the overseer gave us the drug and every day we slaved in the fields for the plantation owner."

Ellie shuffled on the rough seat. "But how did you escape?" she asked.

"To tell the truth I'll never know. The overseer made some kind of mistake. He didn't give us the drug one day and we began to remember who we were. When he came to take us back to the shed where we slept we turned on him and locked him away. Then we went down to the owner's cottage and saw him at work. He was mixing his drugs at a table. We decided to wreck the place. We stepped through the door just as he was picking up a large fish. He saw us walking towards us and screamed. At first I thought he was afraid of us . . . but he clutched at his wrist. Then fell backwards into a chair. A spine from the fish had scratched him as he swung round to see us . . . and the spines were poisoned."

"He killed himself?" the girl asked. "Serves him right."

Clairvius nodded. "It saved many more poor souls being turned into Zombies."

"And now you've come back to get your revenge on your brother?" Josie asked. "What are you going to do to him?"

The old man rose to his feet. The afternoon sun was making long shadows now and the gravestones were bone-white. He stepped through the gate into the graveyard and walked along the rows. At last he came to a halt at a new stone. "I didn't dare come back to L'Estere Village. I knew that François would just find some other way to get rid of me . . . and next time he would make sure I didn't rise from my grave!"

"So why have you come back now?" Ellie asked.

Clairvius answered by nodding at the gravestone. The girls read it. "François Narcisse – Died August 1982."

"That's right. I feel safe to come home now. It's been twenty years. But it's good to come home in the end," the old man said.

Josie looked up at him in wonder. "Were you really buried alive?" she asked.

The old man pointed to a scar on his cheek. "That's where a nail from my coffin went through my cheek," he said. Then he took two steps to his right and looked at another gravestone. It was older and more worn than the other one.

The carved words said: *Clairvius Narcisse, died March 1962. Rest in Peace.*

Zombies — Make up your mind

1. Many people in Haiti believe in Zombies and are sure that it is lucky to touch one. They say that the Zombie is a dead body that is able to move and work by magic. This is often as a punishment for some crime. But people who have talked to former Zombies are sure that there is no magic involved. They believe they might be simply drugged, as Clairvius Narcisse was.

2. The 'Zombie Drug' is said to be a mixture of animal, fish and vegetable matter including sea snake, bouga toad, millipede and tarantula. The poisons from these creatures are mixed with the leaves from the cashew nut plant and poison ivy. Finally the poison from the deadly puffer fish is added. Too much of this poison would kill the victim. Just the right amount may paralyse them long enough to appear dead and be buried. The second drug, the one that turns a person into a slave, is called Zombie's cucumber. It is a mixture of plants including sweet potato and cane sugar.

3. In 1993 a man called André Ville Jean-Paul gathered thousands of people in Haiti football stadiums to hear his story. Mr Jean-Paul said he was seventeen when he had a fit. His family believed he was dead and he was buried. However, after two weeks a bokor (voodoo magician) made his coffin rise through the soil and Jean-Paul was released. The magician turned the young man into a Zombie and made him work in the fields with eighteen other Zombies. Jean-Paul didn't know how long this went on but he was released from the spell when a crazed Zombie beat the master to death.

4. The people of Haiti are very superstitious and sincerely believe in "Voodoo" or Black Magic. In 1994 the military government appointed 81-year-old Emile Jonassaint as president because he was supposed to have magic powers – he could see into the future and spoke the secret Voodoo language. He told people that Haiti was the lost island of Atlantis and he had been chosen to stop it sinking back into the sea. Because of the government's cruelty the Americans invaded Haiti to help the people on 19 September 1994. The government threatened to defend the island with Voodoo magic. They said the American planes would burn in the sky, their ships would sink and soldiers would be turned into Zombies if they landed. It seems as if the power of the American weapons was greater than the power of Voodoo. The Americans took control of the island without much trouble.

5. The people of Haiti take Zombies very seriously. In 1989 a law was passed announcing that Zombie-makers would go to prison for life. Haiti legends say that if you give a Zombie salt he (or she) will recover their memory. There are stories of Zombies who have accidentally been fed salt by their slave masters and remembered who they were. Some say Zombies become uncontrollable and rush to their graves where they try to dig their way back in. On touching the earth they turn to dust.